Pam Wedgwood

Grades 2-3

More Up-Grade!

Light relief between the grades

Spaß und Entspannung mit leichten Originalstücken für Klavier Zweiter Schwierigkeitsgrad
Plaisir et détente avec des pièces originales simples pour piano Niveau 2

For the online audio played by Pam Wedgwood
scan the QR code or go to:
www.fabermusic.com/content/audio

FABER ƒƒ MUSIC

Contents   *page*

© 2006 by Faber Music Ltd
First published in 2006 by Faber Music Ltd
Bloomsbury House
74–77 Great Russell Street
London WC1B 3DA
Cover design by Stik
Music processed by MusicSet 2000
Printed in England by Caligraving Ltd
All rights reserved

ISBN10: 0-571-52421-4
EAN13: 978-0-571-52421-1

To buy Faber Music publications or to find out about the full range of titles available
please contact your local music retailer or Faber Music sales enquiries:

Faber Music Limited, Burnt Mill, Elizabeth Way, Harlow CM20 2HX
Tel: +44 (0)1279 82 89 82   Fax: +44 (0)1279 82 89 83
sales@fabermusic.com   fabermusicstore.com

1. Au matin

4

2. Spider in the bath

*or choose any cluster of notes

3. Scattered showers

4. Blackjack

5. Marionettes

6. Streetwise

7. Trapped

8. Chop 'n' change

9. Floral dance

10. Barley twist

11. Blueberry blues

12. Blue river rag

13. Second thoughts